HAYES®
EXERCISES IN ENGLISH
GRADE THREE

by EVELYN RUDOLPH and C.N. HAYES

This Teacher's Manual has been prepared for the exclusive use of the teacher and is not supplied to pupils at any time.

This Teacher's Manual and Answer Book contains the answers to all of the lessons in Exercises in English for Grade III except those which admit of a variety of answers. This Answer Book has been prepared for the exclusive use of the teacher and should never be allowed in the hands of the pupils.

These Exercises in English have been designed with a two-fold purpose. Essentially they are for the purpose of supplying drill and practice in those items which are included in the average course of study in English for Grade III. Their second purpose is to furnish you with an easy and comprehensive means of testing the pupil's knowledge of these things.

The Exercises have been prepared in a variety of forms in order to avoid monotony as much as possible. They are easily administered and the scoring for most of the questions is objective. A certain number of questions call for individual answers. The teacher will have to decide each of these cases.

At the top of each Exercise — except in the Review Tests — is a summary of the rules or material covered by the Exercise on that page. This may be used for study or for casual reference, whichever is desired. In case the teacher does not want the children to see these rules while they are preparing the exercises, they may be covered by a slip of paper.

The teacher should emphasize the fact that students should not begin work on a lesson until they have read the directions carefully and are positive that they understand exactly what is to be done. The fact that there is quite a variety in the form of the Exercises makes this doubly essential.

Exercises in English for Grade III is the first book in the series of English Exercise books for Grades III to VIII.

EXERCISE 1. Recognizing Sentences
1. no 2. yes 3. no 4. no 5. yes 6. yes 7. no 8. yes 9. no 10. no 11. yes 12. yes 13. no 14. yes 15. no 16. no 17. yes 18. yes

EXERCISE 2. Making Sentences
1-20. Answers to these will vary.

EXERCISE 3. Making Sentences
1-18. Answers to these will vary.

EXERCISE 4. Making Sentences
1-18. Answers to these will vary.

EXERCISE 5. Kinds of Sentences
1. asks 2. asks 3. tells 4. tells 5. tells 6. asks 7. tells 8. asks 9. tells 10. tells 11. asks 12. asks 13. tells 14. asks 15. asks 16. tells 17. asks 18. tells

EXERCISE 6. Marks at the End of a Sentence
1. . 2. ? 3. . 4. . 5. ? 6. . 7. . 8. ? 9. ? 10. . 11. ? 12. ? 13. . 14. ? 15. . 16. ? 17. ? 18. .

EXERCISE 7. Beginning and Ending a Sentence Correctly
1. Sugar eat. 2. My Anne. 3. Helen eyes. 4. Where go? 5. The round. 6. Cows milk. 7. A fire. 8. These mine. 9. Coal black. 10. The tall. 11. He suit. 12. The tired. 13. Roses fence. 14. The dusty. 15. Ice water. 16. Rice South. 17. Some fur. 18. My broken.

EXERCISE 8. Test on Sentences

1. S 2. S 3. N 4. S 5. N 6. S 7. N 8. asks 9. asks 10. tells 11. tells 12. asks 13. tells 14. asks 15. tells 16. asks 17. tells 18. tells

EXERCISE 9. Test On Sentences

1. . 2. . 3. ? 4. ? 5. ? 6. . 7. . 8. . 9. ? 10. .

11-18. Answers will vary.

EXERCISE 10. The Use of Capital Letters

1. This 2. The 3. Mary 4. What 5. I 6. Her 7. You 8. We 9. A 10. Sunday 11. Jane brought her lunch to school. 12. The boys played in the street. 13. What has legs but can't walk? 14. Seven and four make eleven. 15. Can you tell me her name?

EXERCISE 11. The Use of Capital Letters

1. John Paul Jones 2. Frank Allen White 3. Mary Jane Parks 4. Alice Jean Smith 5. James Henry Brown 6. Lewis Allen Carrol 7-9. Answers will vary. 10. We talked to Marie's uncle. 11. Who was George Washington? 12. Frank, Jane, and Tom know Mr. Smith.

EXERCISE 12. The Use of Capital Letters

1. New York City 2. Front Street 3. Chicago, Illinois 4. Grand Avenue 5. Detroit, Michigan 6. Cherry Street 7-9. These answers will vary. 10. We live on Clark Street. 11. Many cars are made in Detroit. 12. Frank lives at 231 Tenth Street, Boston.

EXERCISE 13. The Use of Capital Letters

1. Father and I played baseball. 2. Frank and I played the game. 3. Mother and I saw the parade. 4. Fred asked if I lost the pen. 5-12. I 13-14. Answers will vary.

EXERCISE 14. The Use of Capital Letters

1. Friday 2. Monday 3. Christmas 4. December 5. June 6. Thanksgiving 7. Tuesday 8. March 9. April 10. Wednesday 11. May 12. July 13. Saturday Sunday 14. November 15. Answers will vary. 16. The first day of the week is Sunday. 17. The first month of the year is January.

EXERCISE 15. The Use of Capital Letters

1. Robert J. Anderson 2. Charles K. Smith 3. Frank W. Johnson 4. Robert L. Stevenson 5. William F. Hopkins 6. Nina W. Putnam 7. James H. Bales 8. Helen R. Davis 9. B. F. Harrison 10. J. Q. Adams 11. T. M. McGraw 12. H. C. Barnes 13. H. P. Watson 14. M. A. B. 15. E. J. L. 16. S. E. J. 17. F. A. T.

EXERCISE 16. The Use of Capital Letters

Mary had a little lamb,
Its fleece was white as snow,
And everywhere that Mary went
The lamb was sure to go.

Old Mother Hubbard went to the cupboard
To get her poor dog a bone,
But when she got there
The cupboard was bare,
And so the poor dog got none.

EXERCISE 17. Test on the Use of Capital Letters

1. Who lives in the new house? 2. He works on Monday, Tuesday, Wednesday, Thursday, and Friday. 3. John and I do not go to school on Thanksgiving, Christmas, Washington's Birthday, and Memorial Day. 4. Mr. J. E. Foreman lives at 19 Adams Street, Bowling Green, Ohio. 5. June, July, and August are summer months. December, January, and February are winter months.

EXERCISE 18. Test on the Use of Capital Letters

1. John Robert White 2. Thanksgiving Day 3. Akron, Ohio 4. Fifth Avenue 5. March, May, June 6. Friday, Monday 7. Frank A. Jones lives in Illinois. 8. Jane and I live on Chestnut Street. 9. On Saturday we went to Gary, Indiana. 10. Christmas is the best holiday. 11. Have you ever seen Cedar Lake? 12. Paris is the capital of France.

EXERCISE 19. Singular and Plural Words

1. dogs 2. cats 3. apples 4. tables 5. pencils 6. flowers 7. letters 8. words 9. trains 10. brothers 11. shoes 12. boards 13. houses 14. keys 15. tails 16. tomatoes 17. hands 18. Negroes 19. coats 20. oranges 21. days 22. toys 23. monkeys 24. beds 25. berries 26. cakes 27. rabbits 28. streets 29. balls 30. wagons

EXERCISE 20. Singular and Plural Words

1. nails 2. knives 3. knee 4. toe 5. men 6. women 7. ruler 8. ships 9. pig 10. river 11. ladies 12. fences 13. robin 14. mouths 15. fathers 16. fish 17. dish 18. faces 19. papers 20. carrot 21. lions 22. stick 23. roof 24. name 25. churches 26. lights 27. bottle 28. story 29. night 30. pictures

EXERCISE 21. Singular and Plural Words

1. skates 2. marbles 3. books 4. ships 5. sheep 6. cherries 7. clowns 8. pies 9. deer 10. berries 11. eyes 12. ears 13. beans 14. cities 15. squirrels 16. towns 17. mice 18. children 19. ring 20. bear 21. potato 22. fox 23. chicken 24. tomato 25. tooth 26. fish 27. frog 28. minute 29. berry 30. man 31. valley 32. goose 33. sky 34. place 35. foot 36. weed

EXERCISE 22. Abbreviations

1. doz. 2. pt. 3. Mon. 4. in. 5. lb. 6. Fri. 7. Jan. 8. yd. 9. ft. 10. gal. 11. qt. 12. Wed. 13. Mr. 14. Sat. 15. pk. 16. St. 17. Aug. 18. Dr. 19. The weight of 1 pt. of water is about 1 lb. 20. We go to school from Mon. until Fri. 21. Our house is on Susan St. 22. Will 2 doz. eggs cost one dollar or more?

EXERCISE 23. Abbreviations

1. The 25 of August was on Friday. 2. There are 4 quarts in 1 gallon. 3. Mr. Brown bought 2 pounds of candy. 4. They came on Monday, February 15, 1930. 5. How many feet are there in 1 yard? 6. Doctor Martin lives on Tenth Street. 7. pounds 8. pint 9. Tuesday 10. September 11. Street 12. October 13. Sunday 14. inch 15. peck 16. gallons

EXERCISE 24. Writing Titles for Names

1. Mr. Arthur Jackson 2. Mr. James Ross 3. Miss Barbara Clark or Ms. Barbara Clark 4. Miss Anne King or Ms. Anne King 5. Mr. Fred Johnson 6. Mrs. Mae Myers or Ms. Mae Myers 7-10. Answers will vary.

EXERCISE 25. Writing Dates

1. (1) The day of the week (2) The day of the month (3) The month of the year (4) The year 2. (1) Tuesday, April 6, 1934 (2) Tuesday, April 13, 1934 (3) Tuesday, April 20, 1934 (4) Tuesday, April 27, 1934 3. (1) Will vary (2) Will vary 4. Friday, April 16, 1934

EXERCISE 26. The Use of A and An

1. a 2. a 3. an 4. a 5. an 6. an 7. an 8. an 9. a 10. a 11. a 12. an 13. An 14. A 15. an 16. a 17. a 18. an 19. an 20. a new . . . an ugly . . . a box . . . an interesting

EXERCISE 27. The Use of Is and Are

1. are 2. are 3. is 4. is 5. are 6. is 7. are 8. is 9. are 10. are 11. are 12. is 13. are 14. are 15. Are 16. are 17. is 18. are

EXERCISE 28. The Use of Was and Were

1. were 2. was 3. Were 4. was 5. were 6. was 7. was 8. were 9. was 10. were 11. were 12. was 13. were 14. was 15. were 16. was 17. were 18. Were

EXERCISE 29. The Use of Break, Broke, and Broken

1. broke 2. broken 3. break 4. broken 5. broken 6. broke 7. broken 8. broken 9. broken 10. broken 11. broken 12. break or broke 13. broke or break 14. broken 15. broken 16. broke 17. broke 18. broken 19. broken

EXERCISE 30. The Use of See, Saw, and Seen
(The words given are the ones which should not be crossed out.)

1. saw 2. see 3. seen 4. saw 5. seen 6. saw 7. seen 8. seen 9. saw 10. seen 11. seen 12. seen 13. seen 14. saw 15. see 16. see or saw 17. saw 18. seen 19. saw or see 20. seen

EXERCISE 31. The Use of Speak, Spoke, and Spoken

1. speak 2. speak 3. spoken 4. spoke 5. spoken 6. spoken 7. spoken 8. spoken 9. spoke 10. spoken 11. speak 12. spoken 13. speak or spoke 14. spoke or speak 15. spoke 16. spoke 17. spoken 18. speak 19. spoken

EXERCISE 32. The Use of Fly, Flew, and Flown

1. fly 2. flown 3. flew 4. flown 5. flown 6. fly 7. flown 8. flew 9. fly 10. flown 11. flown 12. flew 13. fly 14. flown 15. flew 16. flew 17. flown

EXERCISE 33. The Use of Throw, Threw, and Thrown

1. threw 2. throw 3. thrown 4. threw 5. threw 6. throw 7. threw 8. thrown 9. thrown 10. thrown 11. wrong 12. correct 13. correct 14. correct 15. wrong 16. correct 17. wrong 18. correct

EXERCISE 34. The Use of I and Me

1. I 2. me 3. me 4. me 5. I 6. I 7. me 8. me 9. I

1. X 2. X 3. O 4. X 5. O 6. O

EXERCISE 35. The Use of He and She, and Him and Her

1. he 2. her 3. him 4. She, him 5. He, she 6. she 7. him 8. she 9. her 10. him, her 11. her 12-15. Answers will vary.

EXERCISE 36. The Use of Isn't and Aren't

1. aren't 2. isn't 3. aren't 4. Isn't 5. Aren't 6. aren't 7. aren't 8. Aren't 9. isn't 10. aren't 11. Isn't 12. isn't 13. Aren't 14. aren't 15. aren't 16. aren't 17. Aren't 18. Isn't

EXERCISE 37. The Use of There Is and There Are

1. There is 2. There are 3. there are 4. There are 5. Are there 6. Are there 7. there are 8. there are 9. there are 10. Is there 11. there is 12. are there 13. There are 14. Is there 15. There are 16. There is 17. There are 18. There is

EXERCISE 38. The Use of There Isn't and There Aren't

1. There isn't 2. there aren't 3. there aren't 4. there isn't 5. There aren't 6. There isn't 7. There isn't 8. There aren't 9. There aren't any apples on the plate. 10. There isn't a cat in the yard. 11. There isn't someone calling. 12. There aren't any flowers on the table.

EXERCISE 39. The Use of Do, Did, and Done

1. did 2. done 3. did 4. done 5. done 6. done 7. do 8. done 9. done, done 10. done 11. You should not have done it. 12. Who did this painting? 13. The man who did the work has gone. 14. John has done his best in the race.

EXERCISE 40. The Use of Know, Knew, and Known

1. know 2. know 3. known 4. known 5. knew 6. known 7. know 8. known 9. know or knew, known 10. know, knew 11. known 12. knew 13. correct 14. wrong 15. correct 16. wrong 17. correct

EXERCISE 41. The Use of Come and Came

1. come 2. come 3. come 4. come 5. came, come 6. come 7. come 8. came 9. came 10. came 11. come 12. come 13. came 14. come 15. Come 16. come 17. come 18. come

EXERCISE 42. The Use of Write, Wrote, and Written

1. write 2. written 3. wrote 4. written 5. write 6. wrote 7. written 8. written 9. written 10. written 11. written 12. write or wrote 13. write 14. written 15. written 16. wrote 17. written 18. written

Exercise 1
RECOGNIZING SENTENCES

When you express a complete thought in words you use a **sentence.** If the group of words does not express a complete thought it is **not a sentence.**

In the following list, draw a line under YES if the group of words is a SENTENCE and draw a line under NO if it is NOT A SENTENCE.

1. The big apples.   yes   no

2. The big apples are red.   yes   no

3. While supper was.   yes   no

4. A large brown bug.   yes   no

5. On the grass lay a shiny penny.   yes   no

6. Who spilled the ink?   yes   no

7. The blue moon.   yes   no

8. Ice is cold.   yes   no

9. The bright lights.   yes   no

10. Four small boys.   yes   no

11. Sunday is the first day of the week.   yes   no

12. Can you tell me whose picture is here?   yes   no

13. Seven and.   yes   no

14. Six is twice three.   yes   no

15. In the nest a baby robin.   yes   no

16. When the wind blows.   yes   no

17. The fire is warm and bright.   yes   no

18. A sentence expresses a complete thought.   yes   no

Exercise 2
MAKING SENTENCES

Use each of these words in a short sentence of your own. Your sentence may either tell something or ask a question.

1. basket _____

2. truck _____

3. fun _____

4. party _____

5. wagon _____

6. ten _____

7. sell _____

8. plant _____

9. visit _____

10. goat _____

11. car _____

12. fire _____

13. ice cream _____

14. dozen _____

15. letter _____

16. package _____

17. me _____

18. that _____

19. school _____

20. come _____

Exercise 3
MAKING SENTENCES

Each of the following is a part of a sentence, only. Make a complete sentence out of each of these by adding words. Your sentence may either tell something or ask a question.

1. My sister _____

2. Two horses _____

3. Did you ever _____

4. The three boys _____

5. Marie walked _____

6. The teacher read _____

7. Skating on the ice _____

8. Elephants and kangaroos _____

9. Theodore Roosevelt was _____

10. How many _____

11. The store on the corner _____

12. My new toys _____

13. The leaves of my book _____

14. This car has black _____

15. In the corner _____

16. Did you see _____

17. Edith's new dress _____

18. Four men _____

MAKING SENTENCES

Use each of these words in a short sentence of your own.

1. door _____

2. walk _____

3. above _____

4. go _____

5. meat _____

6. coat _____

7. milk _____

8. smoke _____

Each of the following is a part of a sentence, only. Make a complete sentence out of each of these by adding words.

9. The box _____

10. In the cage was _____

11. The windows of the store _____

12. We bought _____

13. The newspapers _____

14. _____ on a chair.

15. _____ out of the chimney.

16. In the morning _____

17. _____ a new hat.

18. At four o'clock _____

Exercise 5
KINDS OF SENTENCES

Some **sentences** tell something. Example: **It is warm today.**
Some **sentences** ask a question. Example: **Did you see the little
dog?**

*Read the following sentences. If the SENTENCE tells something, draw
a line under the word TELLS at the end of the sentence. If the SEN-
TENCE asks something, draw a line under the word ASKS.*

1. Is today Friday?   tells   asks

2. Are you going to town?   tells   asks

3. The dog is brown and white.   tells   asks

4. My pencil is broken.   tells   asks

5. My little sister is four years old.   tells   asks

6. How old is your sister?   tells   asks

7. Christmas comes in December.   tells   asks

8. Did you put the books in the case?   tells   asks

9. It is raining.   tells   asks

10. The man drove slowly down the street.   tells   asks

11. Did you see the fire?   tells   asks

12. Should a sentence begin with a capital?   tells   asks

13. Jocko was a monkey.   tells   asks

14. Do you get plenty of fresh air?   tells   asks

15. Why do we celebrate the 4th of July?   tells   asks

16. The cows were in the pasture.   tells   asks

17. Do you like candy?   tells   asks

18. Chicago is a large city.   tells   asks

Exercise 6
MARK AT THE END OF A SENTENCE

A **period** should be placed at the end of a sentence which tells something.

A **question mark** should be placed at the end of a sentence which asks something.

Put the correct mark after each SENTENCE.

1. I know a girl named Mary _____

2. Does your school have a television set _____

3. An elephant has a long trunk _____

4. You should brush your teeth every day _____

5. In what month is your birthday _____

6. It is snowing today _____

7. Every sentence should begin with a capital letter _____

8. Do you drink plenty of milk _____

9. Do fish live in water _____

10. Christmas trees are green _____

11. What color is a mouse _____

12. Did you ever see a woodpecker _____

13. My kitten is black and white _____

14. Do you like tomatoes _____

15. My doll has a pink dress _____

16. Is the sky blue _____

17. What games do you play at school _____

18. Thanksgiving comes in November _____

6

BEGINNING AND ENDING A SENTENCE CORRECTLY

Begin each of these sentences correctly by writing in the blank the word found in the column at the left.

Then end each sentence correctly by writing in the blank the word found in the column at the right. Be sure to put the correct pronunciation mark at the end of the sentence.

1. sugar _____ is good to _____ eat

2. my _____ doll is named _____ Anne

3. Helen _____ has blue _____ eyes

4. where _____ did he _____ go

5. the _____ moon is _____ round

6. cows _____ give _____ milk

7. a _____ house is on _____ fire

8. these _____ eggs are _____ mine

9. coal _____ is _____ black

10. the _____ policeman is _____ tall

11. he _____ wears a blue _____ suit

12. the _____ men are _____ tired

13. roses _____ grow on the _____ fence

14. the _____ road is _____ dusty

15. ice _____ is frozen _____ water

16. rice _____ grows in the _____ South

17. some _____ animals have _____ fur

18. my _____ pen is _____ broken

7

Exercise 8
TEST ON SENTENCES

Place an S before each of the following which is a SENTENCE.
Place an N before each which is NOT A SENTENCE.

————————————— 1. Who is driving that automobile?

————————————— 2. Where is your school?

————————————— 3. How many children?

————————————— 4. There are ten dimes in a dollar.

————————————— 5. The heavy black clouds.

————————————— 6. A large wave swept over the boat.

————————————— 7. Struck the train.

Write TELLS before each sentence which tells something.
Write ASKS before each sentence which asks something.

————————————— 8. Did you ever see a fairy?

————————————— 9. What do bears do in the winter?

—————————————10. Mr. Frog has a deep voice.

—————————————11. Silk comes from Japan.

—————————————12. From what country do we get coffee?

—————————————13. Crows are black.

—————————————14. Do Dutch people wear wooden shoes?

—————————————15. Much sugar comes from Cuba.

—————————————16. What time is it?

—————————————17. It is three o'clock.

—————————————18. Discovery Day comes on October 12.

8

Exercise 9
TEST ON SENTENCES

Put the proper mark at the end of each of these sentences.

1. The floor is covered with rugs _____

2. The walls of the room are painted green _____

3. Which are the spring months _____

4. Did you get your feet wet _____

5. Are these apples sour _____

6. Bobby has a pet squirrel _____

7. The lake is covered with ice _____

8. We are planning a camping trip this summer _____

9. Do you like to make snowballs _____

10. Jim's dog is bringing home the cows _____

Use each of these words correctly in a short sentence which tells something. Put the correct mark at the end.

11. sleep _____ .

12. tent _____ .

13. music _____ .

14. chicken _____ .

Use each of these words correctly in a short sentence which asks something. Put the correct mark at the end.

15. hungry _____ .

16. birthday _____ .

17. officer _____ .

18. breakfast _____ .

9

Exercise 10
THE USE OF CAPITAL LETTERS
THE FIRST WORD IN A SENTENCE

The first word in a sentence should begin with **a capital letter.**
Complete each sentence by writing the word correctly in the blank.

1. _____ boy has several marbles   this

2. _____ wind is cold.   the

3. _____, where is my coat?   mary

4. _____ is in the basket?   what

5. _____ have not had my lunch.   i

6. _____ hair is black.   her

7. _____ should pick up your papers.   you

8. _____ saw seven new houses.   we

9. _____ pencil is needed for this lesson.   a

10. _____ is a holiday.   sunday

Rewrite each sentence and make CAPITAL LETTERS where they should be used.

11. jane brought her lunch to school.

_____

12. the boys played in the street.

_____

13. what has legs but can't walk?

_____

14. seven and four make eleven.

_____

15. can you tell me her name?

_____

Exercise 11
THE USE OF CAPITAL LETTERS
THE NAME OF A PERSON

Each word in the **name of a person** should begin with a **capital letter.**

Rewrite these names and use CAPITAL LETTERS where they should be used.

1. john paul jones _____

2. frank allen white _____

3. mary jane parks _____

4. alice jean smith _____

5. james henry brown _____

6. lewis allen carrol _____

Write the following names correctly.

7. Your full name. _____

8. The full name of a man you know. _____

   _____

9. The full name of a woman you know _____

   _____

Rewrite each sentence and make CAPITAL LETTERS where they should be used.

10. We talked to marie's uncle.

    _____

11. Who was george washington?

    _____

12. frank, jane, and tom know Mr. smith.

    _____

Exercise 12
THE USE OF CAPITAL LETTERS
THE NAMES OF PLACES

The **names of places** should begin with **capital letters.**

Rewrite these names and use CAPITAL LETTERS where they should be used.

1. new york city _____

2. front street _____

3. chicago, illinois _____

4. grand avenue _____

5. detroit, michigan _____

6. cherry street _____

Write the following names correctly.

7. The name of the town in which you live

_____

8. The name of the nearest large city

_____

9. The name of a street which you know

_____

Rewrite each sentence and make CAPITAL LETTERS where they should be used.

10. We live on clark street.

_____

11. Many cars are made in detroit.

_____

12. Frank lives at 231 tenth street, boston.

_____

Exercise 13
THE USE OF CAPITAL LETTERS
THE WORD I

The word I should always be **a capital letter,** when we use it in speaking about ourselves.

Rewrite the following sentences correctly.

1. Father and i played baseball.

   _____

2. Frank and i played the game.

   _____

3. Mother and i saw the parade.

   _____

4. Fred asked if i lost the pen.

   _____

Write the word I in the blank in each sentence.

5. My dog and _____ rode in the truck.

6. The word _____ should always be a capital letter.

7. _____ will ask my mother if _____ can come.

8. Shall _____ write my lesson on this paper?

9. _____ shall put the book in my desk.

10. Charles and _____ are in the same class.

11. Yes, this is _____ .

12. Do you know where _____ put my cap?

Write two sentences, using the word I correctly in each.

13. _____

14. _____

Exercise 14

THE USE OF CAPITAL LETTERS
DAYS OF WEEK, MONTHS, HOLIDAYS

The names of the **days of the week,** the **months of the year,** and of **holidays** should begin with **capitals.**

Rewrite these names and use CAPITAL LETTERS where they should be used.

1. friday _____
2. monday _____
3. christmas _____
4. december _____
5. june _____
6. thanksgiving _____

7. tuesday _____
8. march _____
9. april _____
10. wednesday _____
11. may _____
12. july _____

Write the following names correctly.

13. The two days of the week on which you do not go to school

_____

14. The name of the month in which Thanksgiving comes

_____

15. The name of the two holidays which you like best

_____

Rewrite each sentence and make CAPITAL LETTERS where they should be used.

16. The first day of the week is sunday.

_____

_____

17. The first month of the year is january.

_____

_____

14

Exercise 15

THE USE OF CAPITAL LETTERS

INITIALS

The first letter of a person's name is called an **initial**. An initial should always be a **capital**. It should always be followed by **a** period.

Copy these names. Use an INITIAL for each middle name.

Example: John Albert Warner   John A. Warner

1. Robert James Anderson   _____
2. Charles Kent Smith   _____
3. Frank William Johnson   _____
4. Robert Louis Stevenson   _____
5. William Fred Hopkins   _____
6. Nina Wilcox Putnam   _____
7. James Henry Bales   _____
8. Helen Ruth Davis   _____

Sometimes a person's first and middle names **are** written as **initials**.

Write the following names that way. An example is given.

Example: Robert Evans Lee   R. E. Lee

9. Benjamin Franklin Harrison _____
10. John Quincy Adams   _____
11. Thomas Milton McGraw   _____
12. Herbert Claud Barnes   _____
13. Harry Porter Watson   _____

Write the INITIALS for each of the following names.

14. Mary Anne Black   _____
15. Elizabeth Jane Long   _____
16. Sara Esther Jones   _____
17. Fred Andrew Thomas   _____

Exercise 16
THE USE OF CAPITAL LETTERS
THE FIRST WORD IN A LINE OF POETRY

The first word in every line of poetry should begin with a **capital letter.**

Copy the following, and use CAPITAL LETTERS where they should be used.

Mary had a little lamb,
its fleece was white as snow,
and everywhere that Mary went
the lamb was sure to go.

---

old Mother Hubbard went to the cupboard
to get her poor dog a bone,
but when she got there
the cupboard was bare,
and so the poor dog got none.

TEST ON THE USE OF CAPITAL LETTERS

Rewrite each of these sentences and use CAPITAL LETTERS where they should be used.

1. who lives in the new house?

   _____

   _____

2. he works on monday, tuesday, wednesday, thursday, and friday.

   _____

   _____

3. john and i do not go to school on thanksgiving, christmas, washington's birthday, and memorial day.

   _____

   _____

   _____

   _____

4. mr. j. e. foreman lives at 19 adams street, bowling green, ohio.

   _____

   _____

5. june, july, and august are summer months.   december, january, and february are winter months.

   _____

   _____

   _____

Exercise 18
TEST ON THE USE OF CAPITAL LETTERS

Rewrite these names and use CAPITAL LETTERS where they should be used.

1. john robert white _____

2. thanksgiving day _____

3. akron, ohio _____

4. fifth avenue _____

5. march, may, june _____

6. friday, monday _____

Rewrite the following sentences and use CAPITAL LETTERS where they should be used.

7. frank a. jones lives in illinois.

   _____

8. jane and i live on chestnut street.

   _____

9. on saturday we went to gary, indiana.

   _____

   _____

10. christmas is the best holiday.

    _____

11. have you ever seen cedar lake?

    _____

12. paris is the capital of france.

    _____

18

Exercise 19
SINGULAR AND PLURAL WORDS

A word which means one person or one thing is a **singular word**. A word which means more than one person or thing is a **plural word**.

The **plural** of most words is made by adding **s** to the singular.

Example: **chairs** is the plural of chair and is formed by adding s. However, in some cases the plural is formed by adding **es or ies** to make the plural. Example: **potatoes** is the plural of potato and is formed by adding **es**. **Pennies** is the plural of penny.

Write the PLURAL of each of the following words.

Singular	Plural	Singular	Plural
1. dog	_____	16. tomato	_____
2. cat	_____	17. hand	_____
3. apple	_____	18. Negro	_____
4. table	_____	19. coat	_____
5. pencil	_____	20. orange	_____
6. flower	_____	21. day	_____
7. letter	_____	22. toy	_____
8. word	_____	23. monkey	_____
9. train	_____	24. bed	_____
10. brother	_____	25. berry	_____
11. shoe	_____	26. cake	_____
12. board	_____	27. rabbit	_____
13. house	_____	28. street	_____
14. key	_____	29. ball	_____
15. tail	_____	30. wagon	_____

19

Exercise 20
SINGULAR AND PLURAL WORDS

A word which means one person or one thing is a **singular word**.

A word which means more than one person or thing is **a plural word**.

The **plural** of most words is formed by adding s, es, or ies to the singular. However, in some cases in order to form the plural the spelling of the entire word must be changed.

Example: **knives** is the plural of **knife.**

It is true, also, that the plural of some words is the same as the singular:

Example: **deer** is either singular or plural.

In the following list, sometimes the SINGULAR is given and sometimes the PLURAL is given. You are to write whichever form is not given.

Singular	Plural	Singular	Plural
1. nail	_____	16. fish	_____
2. knife	_____	17. _____	dishes
3. _____	knees	18. face	_____
4. _____	toes	19. paper	_____
5. man	_____	20. _____	carrots
6. woman	_____	21. lion	_____
7. _____	rulers	22. _____	sticks
8. ship	_____	23. _____	roofs
9. _____	pigs	24. _____	names
10. _____	rivers	25. church	_____
11. lady	_____	26. light	_____
12. fence	_____	27. _____	bottles
13. _____	robins	28. _____	stories
14. mouth	_____	29. _____	nights
15. father	_____	30. picture	_____

Exercise 21
SINGULAR AND PLURAL WORDS

A word which means one person or thing is a **singular word**.
A word which means more than one person or thing is a **plural word**.

Write the PLURAL of the following words.

Singular	Plural	Singular	Plural
1. skate	_____	10. berry	_____
2. marble	_____	11. eye	_____
3. book	_____	12. ear	_____
4. ship	_____	13. bean	_____
5. sheep	_____	14. city	_____
6. cherry	_____	15. squirrel	_____
7. clown	_____	16. town	_____
8. pie	_____	17. mouse	_____
9. deer	_____	18. child	_____

Write the SINGULAR of each of the following words.

19. _____ rings		28. _____ minutes	
20. _____ bears		29. _____ berries	
21. _____ potatoes		30. _____ men	
22. _____ foxes		31. _____ valleys	
23. _____ chickens		32. _____ geese	
24. _____ tomatoes		33. _____ skies	
25. _____ teeth		34. _____ places	
26. _____ fish		35. _____ feet	
27. _____ frogs		36. _____ weeds	

ABBREVIATIONS

An **abbreviation** is a short way of writing a word. Certain words like inch, pint, dozen, the days of the week, and the months of the year are often abbreviated. A period should always be placed after an **abbreviation**. For example: **in.** is the abbreviation for inch.

Write the correct ABBREVIATIONS for these words. Be sure to put the correct punctuation mark after the abbreviation.

1. dozen	_____	10. gallon	_____
2. pint	_____	11. quart	_____
3. Monday	_____	12. Wednesday	_____
4. inch	_____	13. Mister	_____
5. pound	_____	14. Saturday	_____
6. Friday	_____	15. peck	_____
7. January	_____	16. Street	_____
8. yard	_____	17. August	_____
9. foot	_____	18. Doctor	_____

Rewrite these sentences and use correct ABBREVIATIONS for the words in black type.

19. The weight of 1 **pint** of water is about 1 **pound.**

_____

20. We go to school from **Monday** until **Friday.**

_____

21. Our house is on Susan **Street.**

_____

22. Will 2 **dozen** eggs cost 50 **cents?**

_____

ABBREVIATIONS
In these sentences you will find certain words **abbreviated**.

Rewrite each sentence and write out each ABBREVIATED WORD in full.

1. The 25 of Aug. was on Fri.

———————————————————————————————

2. There are 4 qts. in 1 gal.

———————————————————————————————

3. Mr. Brown bought 2 lbs. of candy.

———————————————————————————————

4. They came on Mon., Feb. 15, 1930.

———————————————————————————————

5. How many ft. are there in 1 yd.?

———————————————————————————————

6. Dr. Martin lives on 10th St.

———————————————————————————————

Write the word for which each ABBREVIATION stands.

7. lbs. —————————— 12. Oct. ——————————

8. pt. —————————— 13. Sun. ——————————

9. Tues. —————————— 14. in. ——————————

10. Sept —————————— 15. pk. ——————————

11. St. —————————— 16. gals. ——————————

Exercise 24
WRITING TITLES FOR NAMES

The word **Mr.** may be written before the name of a man.
Example: Mr. John Brown

The word **Miss or Ms.** may be written before the name of a woman who is not married.
Example: Miss Marjorie Smith or Ms. Marjorie Smith

The word **Mrs. or Ms.** may be written before the name of a woman who is married.

Rewrite each name and place the correct title before it.

Name with **correct title.**

1. Arthur Jackson _____

2. James Ross _____

3. Barbara Clark (not married) _____

4. Anne King (not married) _____

5. Fred Johnson _____

6. Mae Myers (married) _____

7. Write your own name with proper title **Mr., Miss, Ms.,** or **Mrs.**

_____

8. Write the name of a man you know with proper title.

_____

9. Write the name of a married woman you know with proper title.

_____

10. Write the name of an unmarried woman you know, with proper title.

_____

Exercise 25
WRITING DATES
February, 1934

Sun.	Mon.	Tues.	Wed.	Thu.	Fri.	Sat.
				1	2	3
4	5	6	7	8	9	1 0
1 1	1 2	1 3	1 4	1 5	1 6	1 7
1 8	1 9	2 0	2 1	2 2	2 3	2 4
2 5	2 6	2 7	2 8			

Read the dates from the calendar given above. Be sure that you write them correctly.

Example: What was the date of the first Sunday in the month? **Sunday, February 4, 1934.**

1. What four facts must you tell about a date?

   (1) _____

      (2) _____

         (3) _____

            (4) _____

2. Write the full date of each Tuesday in the month.

   (1) _____

   (2) _____

   (3) _____

   (4) _____

3. Write the full date of two important holidays in this month.

   (1) _____

   (2) _____

4. Write the date of the third Friday in the month.

Exercise 26
THE USE OF A AND AN

You should use **an** before any word which begins with the sound of a, e, i, o, u.

You should use **a** before all other words.

    Example: **an** ink bottle—a beautiful flower

Use **a** *and* **an** *correctly before these words.*

1. _____ man   6. _____ airplane

2. _____ boy   7. _____ orange

3. _____ elephant   8. _____ apple

4. _____ window   9. _____ rabbit

5. _____ hour   10. _____ pencil

Use **A** *and* **AN** *correctly in the blanks in these sentences.*

11. The teacher read us _____ story.

12. That number looks like _____ eight.

13. _____ automobile stood by the curb.

14. _____ girl was sitting in the front seat.

15. The robin is _____ early bird.

16. Jane is _____ beautiful girl.

17. The desk was scratched with _____ knife.

18. The bird flew through _____ open window.

19. We saw _____ old man walking down the street.

20. For Christmas I got _____ new doll, _____ ugly, wooly bear, _____ box of candy, and _____ interesting book.

Exercise 27
THE USE OF IS AND ARE

You should use **is** with a word meaning one person **or thing.**

You should use **are** with a word meaning more than **one person** or thing.

You should always use **are** with **you** whether you mean one **person** or more than one person.

Example: Three little pigs **are** in the pen.
This show **is** old. You **are** too late.

Use **is** *or* **are** *correctly in the blanks in these sentences.*

1. There _____ seven girls in the class.

2. How _____ you going to get home?

3. This book _____ blue and white.

4. The wind _____ cold.

5. How many marbles _____ in the sack?

6. Mary _____ not at home today.

7. Alice and Mary _____ visiting in Chicago.

8. Who _____ president of the the United States?

9. There _____ fifty stars in our flag.

10. The little birds _____ looking for food.

11. You _____ invited to my party tomorrow.

12. Miss White _____ my teacher.

13. My books _____ in my desk.

14. Whose papers _____ these on the floor?

15. _____ there five fingers on each hand?

16. John and I _____ good friends.

17. He _____ a year older than I.

18. Here _____ your colored crayons.

Exercise 28

THE USE OF WAS AND WERE

You should use **was** with a word meaning one person or thing.

You should use **were** with a word or words meaning more than one person or thing.

You should always use **were** with **you** whether one person or more than one person is meant.

Example: The man **was** honest.
Two boys **were** at the gate.
You **were** right.

Use **was** *or* **were** *correctly in the blanks in these sentences.*

1. Two horses _____ in the field.

2. What _____ the answer to the first question?

3. _____ you ever in an airplane?

4. Yes, I _____ in an airplane last summer.

5. Two dogs _____ playing in our yard.

6. One dog _____ black and white.

7. The other _____ brown and tan.

8. These dogs _____ Mr. Brown's.

9. Who _____ Abraham Lincoln?

10. Mother, Father, and I _____ in the park.

11. There _____ many animals there.

12. One cage _____ filled with monkeys.

13. Some of the monkeys _____ eating peanuts.

14. Frank _____ nine years old last Sunday.

15. Where _____ you when the wind blew?

16. I _____ in the house.

17. Several of us _____ playing games.

18. _____ there one or two cats on the porch?

THE USE OF BREAK, BROKE, AND BROKEN

The word **broken** needs a helping word such as **have, has, had.**
The words **break** and **broke** never need a helping word.

*Use **break, broke,** or **broken** correctly in the blanks in these sentences.*

1. Who _____ my ruler?

2. This ruler has been _____.

3. Did your watch _____ when it fell?

4. No, it had been _____ before.

5. Two windows were _____ by the wind.

6. The animals _____ from their cages.

7. Our radio is _____.

8. Tom's radio also is _____.

9. Who has _____ the ink bottle?

10. Walter's arm is _____.

11. The word _____ needs a helping word.

12. The word _____ never needs a helping word.

13. The word _____ never needs a helping word, either.

14. Father has _____ his glasses.

15. Several chairs have been _____.

16. Someone _____ this lock.

17. The dishes _____ when they fell.

18. Was the bicycle _____ when you got it?

19. No, it was not _____ when I got it.

Exercise 30
THE USE OF SEE, SAW, AND SEEN

The word **seen** needs a helping word such as **have, has, had.**
The words **see** and **saw** do not need a helping word.

Cross out the words which should not be used in each sentence.

1. I (see, saw, seen) a friend on the street today.

2. Did you ever (see, saw, seen) a hockey game?

3. Yes, we have (see, saw, seen) one several times.

4. We (see, saw, seen) a football game in the park.

5. It was the first game we had ever (see, saw, seen).

6. Last winter we (see, saw, seen) some rabbits in the snow.

7. I have (see, saw, seen) a brown rabbit and a white one.

8. James had never (see, saw, seen) a white rabbit before.

9. Who (see, saw, seen) my pet dog?

10. I have not (see, saw, seen) it.

11. Mary said she had (see, saw, seen) many big boats.

12. Have you ever (see, saw, seen) a giraffe?

13. The word (see, saw, seen) needs a helping word.

14. The word (saw, seen) does not need a helping word.

15. The word (see, seen) does not need a helping word, either.

16. I (see, saw, seen) a window full of toys in a store.

17. Jean and Alice (see, saw, seen) a good show yesterday.

18. It was one they had never (see, saw, seen) before.

19. I (see, saw, seen) you on the way to school.

20. Have you (see, saw, seen) my purse?

Exercise 31
THE USE OF SPEAK, SPOKE, AND SPOKEN
The word **spoken** needs a helping word such as **have, has, had.**
The words **speak** and **spoke** never need a helping word.

Use **speak, spoke,** *and* **spoken** *correctly in the blanks in these sentences.*

1. May I _____ to Ellen?

2. Yes, you may _____ to Ellen.

3. You have _____ to her once before.

4. The man _____ very quietly.

5. Has John _____ to you about the pony?

6. No, he has not _____ to me yet.

7. What language is _____ in France?

8. You should not have _____ so quickly.

9. A famous poet _____ to our school today.

10. He is the first person who has _____ to the school.

11. Perhaps he will _____ to us again soon.

12. The word _____ needs a helping word.

13. The word _____ does not need a helping word.

14. The word _____ does not need a helping word, either.

15. Who _____ about the valentine box?

16. Jane, Mary, and Betty _____ about it.

17. You should have _____ to Miss Jones.

18. Shall I _____ to Mr. Smith now?

19. Have you _____ for some tickets?

31

Exercise 32
THE USE OF FLY, FLEW, AND FLOWN

The word **flown** needs a helping word such as **have, has,** or **had.**
The words **fly** and **flew** never need a helping word.

*Use **fly, flew,** or **flown** correctly in these sentences.*
Choose the correct word from those in parenthesis at the end of each sentence.

1. Animals walk; birds _____. (fly, flown)

2. Some birds have _____ thousands of miles. (flew, flown)

3. An airplane _____ over the city. (fly, flew)

4. It had _____ from St. Louis. (flew, flown)

5. Several people have _____ across the ocean. (flew, flown)

6. Did you ever _____ a kite? (fly, flew)

7. The papers have _____ away. (flown, flew)

8. They _____ away when the wind blew. (flew, flown)

9. Birds _____ south when winter comes. (fly, flown)

10. Have you ever _____ in an airplane? (flew, flown)

11. Yes, I have _____ twice. (flew, flown)

12. The kite _____ away when the string broke. (flew, flown)

13. Can a rabbit _____ ? (fly, flew)

14. Some dust has _____ into the water. (flown, flew)

15. The sparrow _____ to the tree. (flew, fly)

16. Then it _____ to another tree. (flew, flown)

17. We saw a balloon which had _____ three thousand miles. (fly, flew, flown)

Exercise 33
THE USE OF THROW, THREW, AND THROWN

The word **thrown** needs a helping word such as **have, has,** or **had.**
The words **throw** and **threw** never need a helping word.

Use **throw, threw,** *or* **thrown** *correctly in the blanks in these sentences.*

1. Tom _____ his hat on the chair.

2. Please _____ me the ball.

3. Have you _____ away your papers?

4. Yes, I _____ them into the wastebasket.

5. Who _____ the rock over the fence?

6. How high can you _____ a ball?

7. Yesterday, I _____ it as high as the house.

8. Fred has _____ it higher than the house.

9. Have you ever _____ a ball through a window?

10. Frank asked me if I had _____ the wood on the fire.

Write the word CORRECT before each sentence which is correct.
Write WRONG before each sentence which is not correct.

_____ 11. John has threw a ball through a window.

_____ 12. I have thrown water on the floor.

_____ 13. The teacher said, "Who threw the water on the floor?"

_____ 14. John has thrown his books in the corner.

_____ 15. Have you ever threw a snowball?

_____ 16. The sailor threw a rope to the boy.

_____ 17. Did you threw with your left hand?

_____ 18. No, I always throw with my right hand.

Exercise 34
THE USE OF I AND ME

It is correct to say—**It is I.** It is not correct to say—**It is me.**
It is correct to say—**He gave the book to me.** It is not correct
to say—**He gave the book to I.**

Use the words **I** *and* **me** *correctly in the blanks in these sentences.*

1. You and _____ will make some candy.

2. The pencil was given to _____.

3. Who spoke to _____?

4. Did you want _____ to stay?

5. Did you know it was _____?

6. Yes, this is _____.

7. You may call _____ when you are ready.

8. Were there any letters for _____?

9. The children and _____ will play some games.

When you speak of some other person and yourself, the other
person's name should come first.

Put a cross **(X)** *before each correctly written sentence and a circle* **(O)**
before each incorrectly written sentence.

_____ 1. Mother and I have good times together.

_____ 2. James, Frank, and I played ball.

_____ 3. I and Helen went to the show.

_____ 4. Father said that he and I would play ball.

_____ 5. I and you are early this morning.

_____ 6. I and Bertha can work at the same table.

THE USE OF HE AND SHE, AND HIM AND HER

It is correct to say—**It is he,** or **It is she.**

It is not correct to say—**It is him,** or **It is her.**

It is correct to say—**We gave the money to him,** or **We gave the money to her.**

Use the words he and she, and him and her correctly in the blanks in these sentences.

1. It is _____. (he, him)

2. Was the flower given to _____? (she, her)

3. No, it was given to _____. (he, him)

4. _____ wanted to walk with _____. (She, Her)
   (he, him)

5. _____ and _____ walked down the street together. (He, Him) (she, her)

6. Mother said that _____ and I would buy Father a present. (she, her)

7. The card was sent to _____. (he, him)

8. It is _____. (she, her)

9. We sent the message to _____. (her, she)

10. The teacher wanted to see _____ and _____.
    (he, him) (she, her)

11. Call _____, please. (she, her)

Use each of the following words correctly in a sentence of your own.

12. she _____

13. he _____

14. him _____

15. her _____

Exercise 36
THE USE OF ISN'T AND AREN'T

You should use **isn't** when you mean one person or thing. You should use **aren't** when you mean more than one person or thing.

You should use **aren't** with **you** whether you mean one person or more than one person.

Write the words **isn't** *or* **aren't** *correctly in the blanks in these sentences.*

1. These _____ my shoes.

2. Why _____ the window open?

3. Betty and Joan _____ at school today.

4. _____ that a pretty flower?

5. _____ those flowers pretty?

6. Why _____ you ready for dinner?

7. Mr. and Mrs. Thomas _____ coming.

8. _____ you going to town with us, Frank?

9. Howard, _____ this your package?

10. You _____ able to play today.

11. _____ the gun loaded?

12. No, it _____ loaded.

13. _____ the stars bright!

14. They _____ as bright as they were last night.

15. Did you say you _____ warm enough?

16. Elizabeth and Mary _____ too late for the show.

17. _____ the boys going to sing for us?

18. _____ Miss Jones a good writer?

Exercise 37

THE USE OF THERE IS AND THERE ARE

You should use **there is** and **is there** with words that mean one person or thing.

You should use **there are** and **are there** with words that mean more than one person or thing.

Write the words **there is, is there, there are,** *or* **are there** *correctly in the blanks in these sentences.*

1. _____ a fish in the pool.

2. _____ white clouds in the sky.

3. In a year _____ twelve months.

4. _____ twenty-four hours in a day.

5. _____ any potatoes in the dish?

6. _____ any airplanes in the field?

7. Yes, _____ four airplanes.

8. Will you see if _____ any bottles on the table?

9. Please tell me if _____ any hard problems.

10. _____ some mud on the floor?

11. Yes, _____ some mud on the floor.

12. How many red stripes _____ in our flag?

13. _____ some fine vegetables for dinner.

14. _____ any water in the jug?

15. _____ cows, horses, and chickens in the barn.

16. _____ a new automobile in the garage.

17. _____ seven broken dishes.

18. _____ a fire in the furnace.

THE USE OF THERE ISN'T AND THERE AREN'T

You should use **there isn't** with words that mean one person or thing.

You should use **there aren't** with words that mean more than one person or thing.

Write the words **there isn't** *or* **there aren't** *correctly in the blanks in these sentences.*

1. _____ anyone at home.

2. Charles says _____ any books in his desk.

3. Is it true that _____ any books in your desk, either?

4. I think _____ room for four people.

5. _____ enough ice cream cones for all.

6. _____ a person on the street.

7. _____ a cloud in the sky.

8. _____ many trees on our farm.

Answer these questions. Be sure to use **there isn't** *or* **there aren't** *correctly in answering them.*

9. Are there some apples on the plate?
   (answer)

   _____

10. Is there a cat in the yard?
    (answer)

    _____

11. Is there someone calling?
    (answer)

    _____

12. Are there any flowers on the table?
    (answer)

    _____

THE USE OF DO, DID, AND DONE

The word **done** needs a helping word such as **have, has,** or **had.**
The words **do** and **did** do not need a helping word.

Use the words **do, did,** *or* **done** *correctly in the blanks in these sentences.*

1. Where _____ you get the new wagon?

2. Have you _____ a good deed today?

3. Tom _____ what his mother asked of him.

4. You should have _____ better on the test.

5. Nothing has been _____ to help me.

6. What would you have _____?

7. No one can _____ just as he pleases.

8. Nothing can be _____ without work.

9. What has been _____ cannot be _____ again.

10. See what the rain has _____ to this book.

Rewrite each of these sentences correctly.

11. You should not have did it.

   _____

12. Who done this painting?

   _____

13. The man who done the work has gone.

   _____

14. John has did his best in the race.

   _____

Exercise 40
THE USE OF KNOW, KNEW, AND KNOWN

The word **known** needs a helping word such as **have, has,** or **had**
The words **know** and **knew** do not need a helping word.

Use the words **know, knew,** *or* **known** *correctly in the blanks in these sentences.*

1. I do not _____ that man.

2. Do you _____ how to subtract?

3. Yes, I have _____ how to subtract since last year.

4. I wish that I had _____ this before.

5. Walter said that he _____ his lesson well.

6. Martha should have _____ better.

7. Do you _____ the sum of four and eight?

8. The word _____ needs a helping word.

9. I _____ that I should have _____ that boy.

10. Did James _____ that we _____ he was not ill?

11. I never have _____ a more honest man.

12. I never _____ a more beautiful woman.

Write the word CORRECT before each sentence which is correct.
Write WRONG before each sentence which is not correct.

_____ 13. I knew Mr. Black in New York City.

_____ 14. I have knew him for many years.

_____ 15. Do you know how to cook?

_____ 16. Margaret had knew how to read before she started to school.

_____ 17. You should have known not to throw snowballs.

Exercise 41

THE USE OF COME AND CAME

The word **came** does not need a helping word. Sometimes the word **come** needs a helping word such as **have, has** or **had.**

Use **come** *or* **came** *correctly in the blanks in these sentences.*

1. Please _____ to my house tomorrow.

2. Shall I _____ by myself?

3. Our friends have _____ from the city.

4. They have _____ to stay a week.

5. When I _____ home, Father had _____ from the store.

6. He had _____ on the five o'clock car.

7. Has your new basketball _____?

8. This little dog _____ to school with me.

9. Perhaps he _____ because he was hungry.

10. Heavy snows _____ last winter.

11. Many birds have _____ since it got warm.

12. They have _____ from the south.

13. This package _____ while I was at school.

14. It should have _____ yesterday.

15. _____ here as quickly as you can.

16. I wish you had _____ sooner.

17. The last train has _____ for today.

18. This letter has _____ from Buffalo.

Exercise 42
THE USE OF WRITE, WROTE, AND WRITTEN

The word **written** needs a helping word such as **have, has,** or **had.**
The words **write** and **wrote** never need a helping word.

Use write, wrote, *or* written *correctly in the blanks in these sentences.*

1. Can you _____ neatly?

2. Have you _____ your name on this lesson?

3. Yes, I _____ it at the bottom of the page.

4. Mary has _____ a letter to her grandmother.

5. Grandmother will _____ Mary a letter next week.

6. Who _____ the story of Peter Rabbit?

7. Was it _____ by a man or woman?

8. Our teacher has _____ some numbers on the blackboard.

9. Alice has _____ with ink.

10. Have you ever _____ with ink?

11. No, I never have _____ with ink.

12. I _____ with a lead pencil.

13. You must never _____ on the walls of a room.

14. The word _____ needs a helping word.

15. It is correct to say "had _____."

16. It is not correct to say "had _____."

17. John said he had always _____ with his left hand.

18. Mother said this letter had been _____ last Monday.

THE USE OF GO, WENT, AND GONE

The word **gone** needs a helping word such as **have, has,** or **had.**
The words **go** and **went** do not need a helping word.

Use **go, went,** *or* **gone** *correctly in the blanks in these sentences.*

1. We _____ to the picture show last night.

2. Who _____ with you to the show?

3. Sister and Mother have _____ shopping.

4. Do you _____ to the Washington School?

5. Charles has _____ home.

6. Father has _____ to get a new automobile.

7. I _____ to school every day last year.

8. Every summer I have _____ on a vacation.

9. Once we _____ to Yellowstone Park.

Write the word CORRECT before each sentence which is correct.
Write WRONG before each sentence which is not correct.

_____ 10. Barbara has gone to the picnic.

_____ 11. She went with Betty.

_____ 12. She should have went with Ruth.

_____ 13. We go to Boston yesterday.

_____ 14. Have your parents gone on that big boat?

_____ 15. Yes, they have went on that boat.

_____ 16. Who went on the train?

_____ 17. Three men and four women went on the train.

Exercise 44
THE USE OF TEAR, TORE, AND TORN
The words **tear** and **tore** do not need a helping word.
The word **torn** needs a helping word such as **have, has,** or **had**
Use **tear, tore,** *or* **torn** *correctly in the blanks in these sentences.*

1. The boys have _____ their clothes.

2. Did you _____ this paper?

3. No, the kitten _____ the paper.

4. The flag has been _____ by the wind.

5. The wind had _____ it yesterday.

6. The birds _____ the nest from the limb.

7. This book cover has been _____ .

8. The pages have been _____ , too.

Exercise 45
THE USE OF WEAR, WORE, AND WORN
The words **wear** and **wore** do not need a helping word.
The word **worn** needs a helping word such as **have, has,** or **had**.
Use **wear, wore,** *or* **worn** *correctly in the blanks in these sentences*

1. We _____ warm clothing in winter.

2. You have never _____ that dress before.

3. Yes, I have _____ this dress before.

4. Helen has _____ her new coat.

5. The water has _____ away these rocks.

6. They have been _____ away by the wind, too.

7. Do you _____ a hat?

8. I have _____ a hat today.

Exercise 46
THE USE OF TWO, TO, TOO

The word **two** expresses a number (2).
  Example: I see **two** horses.

The word **to** is used to help express action and to show place.
  Example: We want **to** help. She went **to** town.

The word **too** is used to mean more than enough or also.
  Example: We had **too** much ice cream.

Use **two, to,** *or* **too** *correctly in the blanks in these sentences.*

1. _____ sparrows sat on the fence.

2. The girls were _____ frightened _____ move.

3. Mr. Stevens is going _____ build _____ houses.

4. Three dollars plus _____ dollars will make five dollars.

5. Rover would like _____ go, _____.

6. School was out at _____ o'clock.

7. The show lasted _____ hours.

8. David drank _____ glasses of milk for his lunch.

9. I like _____ study arithmetic.

10. The word _____ means a number.

11. We, _____, would like _____ see the game.

12. The kitten likes _____ play with a string.

13. The word _____ sometimes means also.

14. The word _____ may also mean more than enough.

15. _____ children were trying _____ learn _____ swim.

16. Do you wish _____ leave your name?

17. It rained for _____ days and _____ nights.

Exercise 47

THE USE OF THESE, THOSE, THEM

The words **these** and **those** are used with another word. The word **them** is used by itself.

Example: Who lost **these** papers?
            I lost **those** papers.
            Please pick **them** up.

Use **these, those,** *or* **them** *correctly in the blanks in these sentences.*

1. Do _____ pieces of music belong to you?

2. Will you hand _____ to me?

3. _____ bears are quite tame.

4. What did you give _____ to eat?

5. _____ boys are Frank's playmates.

6. Who brought _____ pumpkins?

7. We will make jack-o-lanterns of _____.

8. Are _____ apples good to eat?

9. Did _____ apples grow in your orchard?

Write CORRECT *before each sentence which is correct, and write* WRONG *before each which is not correct.*

_____ 10. Look at them boats.

_____ 11. We saw them yesterday.

_____ 12. Have them women gone?

_____ 13. Yes, Betty went with them.

_____ 14. How much are these cookies?

_____ 15. We sell them ten cents a dozen.

_____ 16. I will take two dozen of those.

Exercise 48

THE USE OF CAN AND MAY

You should use the word **may** in asking or in giving permission for something.

Example: **May** I have your pen?

You should use the word **can** when you mean to be able to do something.

Example: Harold **can** run.

Use the words **can** *or* **may** *correctly in the blanks in these sentences.*

1. _____ I speak to Betty?

2. _____ you turn a handspring?

3. Yes, I _____ turn a handspring.

4. Boys _____ run.

5. Fred, you _____ have the bottle of milk.

6. John, you _____ be the leader.

7. Who _____ sharpen this crayon?

8. Do you think that I _____ solve this problem?

9. Father, _____ I pass the candy?

Write sentences giving permission or asking permission for the following.

10. To visit a friend's home

_____

11. To buy some oranges

_____

Write sentences showing your ability to do the following.

12. To make a stool

_____

13. To drive an automobile

_____

Exercise 49

TEST ON CORRECT USAGE

Write in the blank the correct form of the word given in parenthesis at the end of the sentence.

1. _____ iron rail lay across the road. (A, An)

2. The board has been _____ in the middle. (broke, broken)

3. Have you _____ the new moon? (seen, saw)

4. _____ seven eggs in the nest. (There is, There are)

5. _____ any period after that sentence. (There isn't, There aren't)

6. Thousands of _____ papers are sold daily. (these, them)

7. It is _____. (her, she)

8. A bicycle has _____ wheels. (too, two)

9. Peter wanted us to throw the apple _____ him. (to, two)

10. We, _____, heard the strange noise. (too, to)

11. _____ you at the circus? (Was, Were)

12. Joan replied, "It is _____." (I, me)

13. The puppies have _____ the clothes. (tore, torn)

14. Marjorie has _____ her new boots. (wore, worn)

15. All of the visitors have _____. (went, gone)

16. Have they _____ home? (went, gone)

17. Dorothy has _____ some wonderful sights. (saw, seen)

18. What has Mary _____ today? (done, did)

Exercise 50
TEST ON CORRECT USAGE

Write in each blank the correct form of the word given in parenthesis at the end of the sentence.

1. California is _____ western state (a, an)

2. Much wheat _____ raised in Kansas. (is, are)

3. My two uncles _____ farmers. (is, are)

4. Dorothy has _____ her new doll. (broke, broken)

5. Who _____ Woodrow Wilson? (was, were)

6. The firemen _____ overcome by smoke. (was, were)

7. Have you _____ our new piano? (saw, seen)

8. You should _____ kindly to the dog. (spoken, speak)

9. The keeper _____ the food to the bears. (threw, throw)

10. You might have _____ a stone across the brook. (threw, thrown)

11. The pilot has _____ his plane upside down. (flew, flown)

12. When Mother came, I had _____ two letters. (wrote, written)

13. Miss Brown _____ slowly across the street. (come, came)

14. I would not have _____ on such a bad night. (come, came)

15. You should have _____ Jane's address. (knew, known)

16. What have you _____ with my golf clubs? (did, done)

17. _____ I ask Martha for her book? (May, Can)

18. I _____ build a toy motor. (can, may)

19. John and Tom _____ brothers. (isn't, aren't)

49

Exercise 51
CONTRACTIONS—RECOGNITION AND USE

Contractions are shortened forms of words or expressions. These shortened forms are made by leaving out some of the letters. Example: **isn't** is a shortened form of **is not**. It is made by leaving out a letter. An apostrophe is put in the place where the letter is left out.

Write the proper CONTRACTION for each of these expressions.

1. is not _____

2. was not _____

3. I am _____

4. are not _____

5. have not _____

6. did not _____

7. could not _____

8. cannot _____

9. do not _____

10. were not _____

Write the words from which each of these CONTRACTIONS was made.

11. can't _____

12. hasn't _____

13. shouldn't _____

14. isn't _____

15. I've _____

16. it's _____

Fill the blanks with the proper CONTRACTIONS chosen from those given above.

17. _____ studying my English lesson now.

18. Father says that I _____ go skating tonight.

19. _____ do that.

20. The children _____ returned yet.

21. Our team _____ win the game.

22. The letter _____ delivered.

23. The peaches _____ good.

Exercise 52

CONTRACTIONS—RECOGNITION AND USE

Contractions are shortened forms of words or expressions. These shortened forms are made by leaving out some of the letters.

Example: **they're** is a shortened form of **they are**. It is made by leaving out a letter. An apostrophe is put in the place where the letter is left out.

Write the proper CONTRACTION for each of these expressions.

1. are not _____

2. was not _____

3. you are _____

4. cannot _____

5. did not _____

6. he is _____

7. we are _____

8. have not _____

Fill the blanks with the proper CONTRACTIONS chosen from those given above.

9. These _____ my crayons.

10. The child _____ hear the car.

11. Fred, _____ you an eraser?

12. _____ coming soon.

Rewrite each sentence. Write as a CONTRACTION the two words in each sentence which may be written that way.

13. James is not a tall boy.

_____

14. We do not care to sing.

_____

15. The horses could not swim.

_____

16. I am sending my mother a book.

_____

Exercise 53

Words Which are Pronounced Alike but Which Have Different Meanings

THE USE OF HEAR AND HERE

Such words as **hear** and **here** sound alike but they are spelled differently and have different meanings. The word **hear** means to use your ears. The word **here** means a place.

Use **hear** *or* **here** *correctly in each sentence.*

1. _____ is the place where the house stood.
2. Did you _____ that shout?
3. We will stay _____ all night.
4. The meeting will be held _____.
5. I like to _____ a good band.

Exercise 54
THE USE OF THERE AND THEIR

The word **there** means a place. The word **their** means possession.

Use **there** *or* **their** *correctly in each sentence.*

1. _____ is the man we want.
2. Over _____ is a good place to camp.
3. The children are washing _____ faces.
4. After that they will eat _____ dinners.
5. The farmers are cutting _____ wheat.

Exercise 55
THE USE OF KNOW AND NO

The word **know** means to have knowledge. The word **no** means not.

Use **know** *or* **no** *correctly in each sentence.*

1. How many people do you _____?
2. There are _____ numbers on this page.
3. _____ one asked any questions.
4. Do you _____ your lesson well?
5. There is _____ cover on this book.

WORDS WHICH ARE PRONOUNCED ALIKE BUT WHICH HAVE DIFFERENT MEANINGS

*fter each word, write another word which is pronounced like the first
ne but which is spelled differently and has a different meaning.*

1. rode _____

2. to _____

3. hear _____

4. deer _____

5. meet _____

6. blew _____

7. eight _____

8. know _____

9. knew _____

10. cent _____

11. bare _____

12. by _____

13. hour _____

14. would _____

15. whole _____

16. peace _____

17. knows _____

18. herd _____

19. sun _____

20. sale _____

Use the correct word in the blank in each sentence.

21. We waited for one _____. (hour, our)

22. The _____ shone brightly. (son, sun)

23. Who _____ you for the groceries? (cent, sent)

24. You have been gone a _____. (weak, week)

25. Betty looks _____. (pail, pale)

26. How much do you _____? (way, weigh)

27. Were there _____ or three boys? (two, to)

28. Did you wish to _____ something? (by, buy)

Exercise 57
WORDS WHICH HAVE THE SAME SOUND
Choose the words from the columns at the right and put them in t
blanks after the words which they sound most like.

1.	race	_____ _____	led	leap
2.	blow	_____ _____	fool	face
3.	more	_____ _____	low	sent
4.	went	_____ _____	past	band
5.	sand	_____ _____	log	fog
6.	deep	_____ _____	tool	sore
7.	dog	_____ _____	case	flow
8.	bed	_____ _____	fed	book
9.	stool	_____ _____	floor	bent
			land	peep

Do the same with this list.

1.	care	_____ _____	hark	pan
2.	hen	_____ _____	sank	fill
3.	red	_____ _____	think	fair
4.	will	_____ _____	heap	light
5.	lark	_____ _____	dead	park
6.	rank	_____ _____	hand	leap
7.	night	_____ _____	pen	den
8.	sink	_____ _____	sight	pink
9.	sheep	_____ _____	hill	head
			frank	hair

54

WORDS WHICH MEAN THE SAME

*raw a line under the word which means about the same as the first
ord of each list.

1.	distant	**near**	far	sharp
2.	journey	plank	farm	trip
3.	discover	find	end	fortune
4.	picture	image	gladness	star
5.	receive	candy	get	pay
6.	overcome	trade	search	conquer
7.	answer	blotter	reply	remain
8.	finish	end	mark	sail
9.	above	near	over	under
0.	late	soon	tardy	fast
1.	fight	say	war	scream
2.	fortunate	afraid	lucky	corner
3.	correct	guess	right	number
4.	exclaim	say	suffer	hear
5.	smooth	soft	slippery	clean
6.	now	forenoon	when	immediately
17.	edge	bottom	rim	top
18.	point	make	show	travel
19.	circle	ring	prompt	explain
20.	firm	solid	beyond	contain

WORDS WHICH MEAN THE SAME AND THOSE WHICH MEAN THE OPPOSITE

If the words mean the SAME, put a letter S in the blank between them

If the words mean the OPPOSITE, put a letter O in the blank between them.

1. warm _____ cold

2. large _____ small

3. high _____ tall

4. ask _____ inquire

5. clean _____ dirty

6. thin _____ narrow

7. heavy _____ light

8. boy _____ girl

9. trip _____ journey

10. up _____ down

11. above _____ over

12. always _____ forever

13. before _____ after

14. wide _____ broad

15. talk _____ speak

16. write _____ erase

17. buy _____ sell

18. black _____ white

VORDS WHICH MEAN THE SAME AND THOSE WHICH MEAN THE OPPOSITE

*'rite beside each word its OPPOSITE. Choose the OPPOSITE from
ιe column at the right.*

1. rich _____ early

2. young _____ poor

3. go _____ wet

4. end _____ heavy

5. beautiful _____ full

6. small _____ old

7. late _____ come

8. empty _____ ugly

9. dry _____ large

beginning

*'rite beside each word another word which MEANS ALMOST THE
'AME. Choose this word from the column at the right.*

1. sick _____ find

2. ask _____ inquire

3. circle _____ ill

4. sad _____ noisy

5. beautiful _____ light

6. discover _____ glad

7. happy _____ new

8. bright _____ unhappy

9. loud _____ ring

pretty

Exercise 61
THE MEANING OF WORDS

Choose the correct words and write them in the blanks. Choose the words from the list given at the bottom of the page.

_____ 1. The sum of five and five

_____ 2. To receive

_____ 3. To leave all alone

_____ 4. To get someone to do as you want him

_____ 5. An Eskimo hut made of ice and snow

_____ 6. To tell what something means

_____ 7. Very large

_____ 8. To hunt for

_____ 9. To go back

_____ 10. Something uncommon

_____ 11. Things to fight with

_____ 12. To say again

_____ 13. A quick look

_____ 14. To stand for

accept	explain	glimpse	igloo
unusual	ten	desert	return
weapons	represent	enormous	
persuade	repeat	search	

HOW, WHERE, WHEN WORDS

Some words show **how** a thing is done. Example: **quickly**

Some words show **where** a person is. Example: **upon**

Some words show **when** something happened. Example: **yesterday**

Write HOW, WHEN, or WHERE in the blank after each word to show what kind of word it is.

1.	quickly	_____	17.	before	_____
2.	now	_____	18.	near	_____
3.	tomorrow	_____	19.	noon	_____
4.	slowly	_____	20.	brightly	_____
5.	there	_____	21.	beside	_____
6.	here	_____	22.	loudly	_____
7.	quietly	_____	23.	forenoon	_____
8.	over	_____	24.	under	_____
9.	inside	_____	25.	today	_____
10.	daytime	_____	26.	afternoon	_____
11.	rapidly	_____	27.	noisily	_____
12.	softly	_____	28.	in	_____
13.	morning	_____	29.	hurriedly	_____
14.	outside	_____	30.	across	_____
15.	night	_____	31.	yesterday	_____
16.	between	_____	32.	upon	_____

Exercise 63
THE CHOICE OF WORDS

Choose the right words from those given below and write them in th blanks.

1. _____ is good to eat.

2. After a rain comes the _____.

3. The _____ is a fierce animal.

4. Would you rather ride upon a pony than upon a _____

5. A _____ is a baby cow.

6. The sea sparkles like a _____.

7. The leaves of the trees were yellow and _____.

diamond	rice	scarlet	rainbow
tiger	train	calf	

In each line is one word which does not belong with the others becaus it does not refer to the same kind of thing. Draw a line under this wor in each line.

1.	corn	wheat	rye	oats	barn
2.	ocean	river	brook	school	lake
3.	horse	cow	pig	bridge	sheep
4.	red	wheel	yellow	blue	orange
5.	lettuce	eggs	shoes	honey	butter
6.	shoes	chair	cap	dress	collar
7.	noon	one	eight	five	two
8.	pencil	pen	crayons	chalk	ruler
9.	peas	beans	milk	radishes	corn
10.	small	large	little	heavy	sunshine

60

Exercise 64
WRITING A FRIENDLY LETTER

Indianapolis, Indiana,
June 14, 1980.

Dear Martha:

Can you come to visit me next week? Mother and I would like to have you. We can go to the fair one day and to the circus on another day. We can have lots of fun if you can come.

Your friend,
Jean

Copy the letter printed above. Be sure to get all of the parts in exactly the right places.

Exercise 65
WRITING A FRIENDLY LETTER

Write a letter to one of your friends, telling her about some interesting thing that has happened. Use the form given below. Use your own name and address.

(Heading)

(Place) _____

(Date) _____

(Greeting)

_____

_____

_____

_____

_____

_____

_____

_____

(Complimentary close) _____

(Signature) _____

Exercise 66
ADDRESSING AN ENVELOPE CORRECTLY

n order to address an envelope correctly, you must write on it
he following things:

1. The name of the person to whom the letter is sent.
2. The number of the house and the name of the street on which this person lives. This is called the street address.
3. The name of the city in which the person lives.
4. The name of the state in which the person lives.

The following is a sample:

Mr. John Young,
14 Adams Street,
Hartford, Wisconsin

Copy this address correctly.

Exercise 67

ADDRESSING AN ENVELOPE CORRECTLY

Address this envelope correctly to Miss Barbara Long, 21 E. Ade Street, Fowler, Indiana.

Remember to put your own name and address in the upper left-hand corner.

Address this envelope correctly to Mr. John Simpson, 400 N. Erie St., Cincinnati, Ohio.

XERCISE 43. The Use of Go, Went, and Gone
went 2. went 3. gone 4. go 5. gone 6. gone 7. went 8. gone 9. went 10. correct 11. correct
. wrong 13. wrong 14. correct 15. wrong 16. correct 17. correct

XERCISE 44. The Use of Tear, Tore, and Torn
torn 2. tear 3. tore 4. torn 5. torn 6. tore 7. torn 8. torn

XERCISE 45. The Use of Wear, Wore, and Worn
wear 2. worn 3. worn 4. worn 5. worn 6. worn 7. wear 8. worn

XERCISE 46. The Use of Two, To, Too
Two 2. too, to 3. to, two 4. two 5. to, too 6. two 7. two 8. two 9. to 10. two 11. too, to
. to 13. too 14. too 15. Two, to, to 16. to 17. two, two

XERCISE 47. The Use of These, Those, and Them
these or those 2. them 3. These or those 4. them 5. Those or these 6. these or those
. them 8. these or those 9. these or those 10. wrong 11. correct 12. wrong 13. correct
. correct 15. correct 16. correct

XERCISE 48. The Use of Can and May
May 2. Can 3. can 4. can 5. may 6. may 7. can 8. can 9. may 10. Use may 11. Use may
. Use can 13. Use can

XERCISE 49. Test on Correct Usage
An 2. broken 3. seen 4. There are 5. There isn't 6. these 7. she 8. two 9. to 10. too
. Were 12. I 13. torn 14. worn 15. gone 16. gone 17. seen 18. done

XERCISE 50. Test on Correct Usage
. a 2. is 3. are 4. broken 5. was 6. were 7. seen 8. speak 9. threw 10. thrown 11. flown
. written 13. came 14. come 15. known 16. done 17. May 18. can 19. aren't

XERCISE 51. Contractions — Recognition and Use
. isn't 2. wasn't 3. I'm 4. aren't 5. haven't 6. didn't 7. couldn't 8. can't 9. don't 10. weren't
. cannot 12. has not 13. should not 14. is not 15. I have 16. it is 17. I'm 18. can't 19. Don't
0. haven't 21. didn't or can't 22. wasn't 23. aren't or weren't

XERCISE 52. Contractions — Recognition and Use
. aren't 2. wasn't 3. you're 4. can't 5. didn't 6. he's 7. we're 8. haven't 9. aren't 10. can't or
idn't 11. haven't 12. He's 13. James isn't a tall boy. 14. We don't care to sing. 15. The horses
ouldn't swim. 16. I'm sending my mother a book.

XERCISES 53, 54, 55. Words Which Are Pronounced Alike But Have Different Meanings
ear or here   1. Here 2. hear 3. here 4. here 5. hear

here or their   1. There 2. there 3. their 4. their 5. their

now or no   1. know 2. no 3. No 4. know 5. no

XERCISE 56. Words Which Are Pronounced Alike But Have Different Meanings
-20. These words will vary with different pupils. 21. hour 22. sun 23. sent 24. week 25. pale
6. weigh 27. two 28. buy

XERCISE 57. Words Which Have the Same Sound
. face case 2. flow low 3. floor sore 4. sent bent 5. land band 6. leap peep 7. log fog
. led fed 9. fool tool

. fair hair 2. pen den 3. dead head 4. fill hill 5. hark park 6. frank sank 7. light sight
. pink think 9. leap heap

EXERCISE 58. Words Which Mean the Same
1. far 2. trip 3. find 4. image 5. get 6. conquer 7. reply 8. end 9. over 10. tardy 11. war 12. lucky 13. right 14. say 15. slippery 16. immediately 17. rim 18. show 19. ring 20. solid

EXERCISE 59. Words Which Mean the Same and Those Which Mean the Opposite
1. O 2. O 3. S 4. S 5. O 6. S 7. O 8. O 9. S 10. O 11. S 12. S 13. O 14. S 15. S 16. O 17. O 18. O

EXERCISE 60. Words Which Mean the Same and Those Which Mean the Opposite
1. poor 2. old 3. come 4. beginning 5. ugly 6. large 7. early 8. full 9. wet

1. ill 2. inquire 3. ring 4. unhappy 5. pretty 6. find 7. glad 8. light 9. noisy

EXERCISE 61. The Meaning of Words
1. ten 2. accept 3. desert 4. persuade 5. igloo 6. explain 7. enormous 8. search 9. return 10. unusual 11. weapons 12. repeat 13. glimpse 14. represent

EXERCISE 62. How, Where, When Words
1. how 2. when 3. when 4. how 5. where 6. where 7. how 8. where 9. where 10. when 11. how 12. how 13. when 14. where 15. when 16. where, when 17. when, where 18. where 19. when 20. how 21. where 22. how 23. when 24. where 25. when 26. when 27. how 28. where 29. how 30. where 31. when 32. where

EXERCISE 63. The Choice of Words
1. Rice 2. rainbow 3. tiger 4. train 5. calf 6. diamond 7. scarlet

1. barn 2. school 3. bridge 4. wheel 5. shoes 6. chair 7. noon 8. ruler 9. milk 10. sunshine

EXERCISE 64. Writing a Friendly Letter

EXERCISE 65. Writing a Friendly Letter

EXERCISE 66. Addressing an Envelope Correctly

EXERCISE 67. Addressing an Envelope Correctly